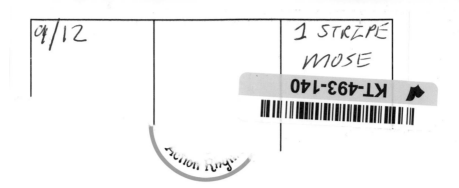

Head, Shoulders, Knees and Toes

and

Clap, Wiggle, Stretch and Jump

Notes for adults

TADPOLES ACTION RHYMES provide support for newly independent readers and can also be used by adults for sharing with young children.

The language of action rhymes is often already familiar to an emergent reader and gives a highly supportive early reading experience.

The alternative rhymes extend this reading experience further, and encourage children to play with language and try out their own rhymes and actions.

If you are reading this book with a child, here are a few suggestions:

1. Make reading fun! Choose a time to read when you and the child are relaxed and have time to share the story.

2. Recite the rhyme together before you start reading. What might the alternative rhyme be about? Why might the child like it?

3. Encourage the child to reread the rhyme, and to retell it in their own words, using the illustrations to remind them what has happened.

4. Point out together the rhyming words when the whole rhymes are repeated on pages 12 and 22 (developing phonological awareness will help with decoding) and encourage the child to make up their own alternative rhymes.

5. Give praise! Remember that small mistakes need not always be corrected.

First published in 2010 by
Franklin Watts
338 Euston Road
London NW1 3BH

Series Editor: Melanie Palmer
Series Advisors: Dr Hilary Minns and Catherine Glavina
Series Designer: Peter Scoulding

Printed in China

Franklin Watts is a division of Hachette Children's Books
an Hachette Livre UK company.
www.hachettelivre.co.uk

ISBN 978 0 7496 9372 5 (hbk)
ISBN 978 0 7496 9378 7 (pbk)

Head, Shoulders, Knees and Toes

Retold by Brian Moses
Illustrated by Lisa Smith

FRANKLIN WATTS
LONDON • SYDNEY

Lisa Smith

"I tried out all the actions in this book and had great fun doing the drawings. I hope that you will enjoy reading it!"

Head

Shoulders

Knees

Toes

Head, shoulders, knees and toes, knees and toes.

Head, shoulders, knees and toes, knees and toes.

7

And eyes and ears
and mouth and nose.

8

eye

ear

mouth

nose

Head, shoulders, knees and toes, knees and toes.

11

Head, Shoulders, Knees and Toes

Head, shoulders, knees and toes,

knees and toes.

Head, shoulders, knees and toes,

knees and toes.

And eyes and ears and mouth and nose.

Head, shoulders, knees and toes,

knees and toes.

Can you point to the rhyming words?

Clap, Wiggle, Stretch and Jump

by Brian Moses
Illustrated by Lisa Smith

13

Brian Moses

"Everyone should do some exercises. I keep fit by walking Honey, my golden labrador, on the hills around our village."

Clap	Wiggle	Stretch	Jump

Clap, wiggle,
stretch and jump,
stretch and jump.

Clap, wiggle,
stretch and jump,
stretch and jump.

17

And sway and wave
and bend and bump.

Clap, wiggle,
stretch and jump,
stretch and jump!

Clap, Wiggle, Stretch and Jump

Clap, wiggle, stretch and jump,

stretch and jump.

Clap, wiggle, stretch and jump,

stretch and jump.

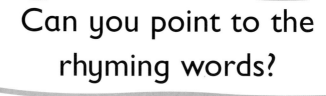

And sway and wave and bend and bump.

Clap, wiggle, stretch and jump,

stretch and jump!

Can you point to the
rhyming words?

Puzzle Time!

1.

2.

3.

Choose the right action
for the picture above.

Answers

The correct action
is number 2.